C000075799

UNDERSTANDING PHONICS BOOK 1

Rita Ray

Contents

Folens Publishers

Phonic elements in Folens *Sounds OK* and *Understanding Phonics*

Phonic element	Sounds OK							Understanding Phonics						
	A	B	C	1	2	3	4	A	B	C	1	2	3	4
consonants b, c, m, t, s, h	●	●	●					●	●	●				
consonants l, d, n, g, f, r, p	●	●	●					●	●	●				
vowels – short a, i	●		●	●				●		●	●			
initial sounds	●		●					●		●				
final sounds	●		●		●			●		●		●		
consonants j, w, x, v, k, y		●		●					●		●			
vowels – short u, o, e		●		●					●		●			
vowel/consonant digraphs		●	●	●	●				●	●	●	●		
double consonants ss, ll, ff		●							●					
consonant blends			●		●	●	●			●		●	●	●
vowel digraphs			●		●	●				●		●	●	
consonant digraphs			●	●		●	●			●	●		●	●
the alphabet				●	●						●	●		
modifying e				●							●			
soft c, g					●	●	●					●	●	●
ph, ch					●								●	
syllables					●	●							●	●
-tion, -sion, -ssion					●	●							●	●
homophones					●	●							●	●
wh, qu					●									●
silent letters					●	●							●	●
suffixes/prefixes					●	●							●	●
-ent, -ant endings					●	●							●	●
-ous, -ary, -ery					●								●	
-act, -uct endings						●								●
-able, -ible endings						●								●

Acknowledgements

Folens allows photocopying of pages marked copiable page for educational use, providing that this use is within the confines of the purchasing institution. Copiable pages should not be declared in any return in respect of any photocopying licence.

Folens books are protected by international copyright laws. All rights are reserved. The copyright of all materials in this book, except where otherwise stated, remains the property of the publisher and author. No part of this publication may be reproduced, stored in a retrieval system, or transmitted, in any form or by any means, for whatever purpose, without the written permission of Folens Limited. This resource may be used in a variety of ways. However, it is not intended that teachers or children should write directly into the book itself.

Rita Ray hereby asserts her moral rights to be identified as the author of this work in accordance with the Copyright, Designs and Patents Act 1988.

Editor: Edward Rippeth   Layout artist: Patricia Hollingsworth
Illustrations: Peter Fox   Cover design: Design for Marketing Ltd

© 1996 Folens Limited, on behalf of the author.
Every effort has been made to contact copyright holders of material used in this book. If any have been overlooked, we will be pleased to make any necessary arrangements.
First published 1996 by Folens Limited, Dunstable and Dublin.
Folens Limited, Albert House, Apex Business Centre, Boscombe Road, Dunstable, LU5 4RL, England.
ISBN 1 85276 830-4

Printed in Singapore by Craft Print.

Introduction

The aim of the activities in this book is to give children an opportunity to focus on phonics. At the early stages of reading and writing, knowing single letter sounds enables children to 'sound out' words and attempt phonetic spelling. *Understanding Phonics Book 1* progresses through long vowel sounds with silent 'e' to a range of letter blends. The activities help children to recognise words and focus on spelling patterns. When phonic needs are identified in the course of classwork, teachers can use this book to meet those needs. The activities presented link reading and writing and help to give children the basic skills and confidence to attempt independent written work.

This resource consists of 44 activities to use mainly with children aged seven to nine, or with children of any age who are at the stage of moving from single letter sounds to learning their first phonic patterns. The pages are photocopiable so they can be used in individual, pair or group contexts.

Although the activities are progressive the teacher can select as required in order to introduce or practise particular phonic patterns with the children.

Each set of activities has a comprehension component. Phonically regular words are used in a way that requires children to show that they understand the words in context. Many children will gain a sense of achievement from being able to build and decode the words. Variety and humour are used to avoid stiltedness and to help children to remember common spelling patterns.

The activities can be used alongside most phonic programmes. The progression followed in this book is based on the graded phonic patterns in *Folens Sounds OK Book 1* but may be used independently. The reinforcement of phonic skills will complement the children's acquisition of literal skills. Please note that where 'u' is read as 'w' it is treated as a consonant, for example, 'qu'.

Word building with $\boxed{a}$

Make new words. Write them on the lines.

b	ag	bag	**c**	ab	cab
	an	_____		an	_____
	ad	_____		ap	_____
	at	_____		at	_____

p	ad	pad	**r**	ag	rag
	al	_____		an	_____
	an	_____		ap	_____
	at	_____		at	_____

s	ad	sad	**m**	ad	mad
	ag	_____		ap	_____
	at	_____		an	_____
	ap	_____		at	_____

n	ag	nag	**h**	ad	had
	ab	_____		am	_____
	an	_____		as	_____
	ap	_____		at	_____

Word building with $\boxed{a}$

Read the words. Draw a picture.

A bat in a cap has a nap on dad's lap.	A sad cat in a mad hat.
My pal Sam has ham and jam.	The gas man ran to the van.
My dad's cat had a jab on the mat.	My dad's cat was mad at dad.

Word building with $\boxed{a}$

Wordsearch
Find 9 words with 'a' in them. Colour them yellow.

c	a	t	x	e	n	h	a	d	u	y	t
b	o	t	r	a	n	p	i	p	o	p	o
m	a	n	y	u	r	s	a	t	m	k	t
l	p	a	n	z	b	k	j	f	h	t	y
m	a	d	b	g	h	s	a	d	l	k	u
j	u	t	r	a	t	m	i	k	i	l	o

Did you find these words? Put them in the right boxes.

sat	ran	cat
pan	rat	man
mad	sad	had

__an	__ad	__at

UNDERSTANDING PHONICS – *Book 1*

Test 1

Write your name: _____

Write your name in the gaps. Read the sentences.

1. _____ has a hat.

2. _____ ran and ran to the van.

3. _____ has jam and a can of ham.

4. _____ can pat a fat rat.

5. _____ and the sad cat had a nap.

6. _____ sat on a pan on the mat.

Draw a picture for one sentence.

Circle the right word for the pictures below.

cap   tap   pan   can   hat   mat

rag   bag   rat   bat   jam   ham

Word building with e

Make new words. Write them on the lines.

l	eg	leg
	et	___
	ed	___

b	ed	bed
	eg	___
	et	___

p	eg	peg
	en	___
	et	___

w	eb	___
	et	___

y	et	___
	es	___

h	en	___
	em	___

Make new words. Write them on the lines.

v	**et**	vet
w		___
y		___
l		___

g	**et**	get
s		___
m		___
n		___

d	**en**	den
h		___
m		___
t		___

l	**eg**	leg
p		___
k		___
b		___

Word building with e

Read the words. Draw a picture.

Let the pet get the vet.	A red hen has ten pens.
A wet pet in a net.	Ted fed Rex in a den.
Ten red hens get in bed.	Ben met ten pets on a jet.

Word building with $\boxed{e}$

Wordsearch

Find 9 words with 'e' in them. Colour them yellow.

m	h	x	l	e	t	p	y	t	n	j	t
h	e	n	k	j	y	l	e	g	k	m	y
k	y	p	b	e	g	m	l	k	p	e	g
b	n	h	g	e	t	w	q	t	b	e	t
m	g	f	d	e	n	q	w	t	p	p	y
q	w	w	y	r	m	e	n	l	u	u	p

Did you find these words? Put them in the right boxes.

den	let	beg
leg	hen	get
bet	peg	men

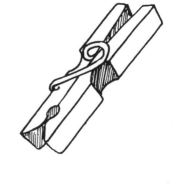

__en	__eg	__et

UNDERSTANDING PHONICS – *Book 1*

Test 2

Write your name: _____

Write your name in the gaps. Read the sentences.

1. _____ met a wet pet.

2. Let_____ get a red pen.

3. _____ and ten men get the jet.

4. "Get in bed,_____."

5. _____ fed ten red hens in a pen.

6. _____ met Ben in a den.

Draw a picture for one sentence.

Circle the right word for the pictures below.

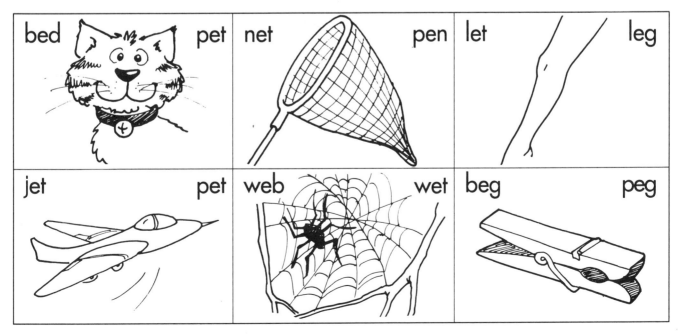

| bed ... pet | net ... pen | let ... leg |
| jet ... pet | web ... wet | beg ... peg |

Word building with $\boxed{\text{i}}$

Make new words. Write them on the lines.

f	ig	fig
	in	_____
	it	_____
	ix	_____

h	id	hid
	im	_____
	it	_____
	ip	_____

b	in	bin
	ig	_____
	it	_____
	ib	_____

d	ip	dip
	im	_____
	in	_____
	ig	_____

Make new words. Write them on the lines.

n	ib	nib
	ip	_____

p	ig	pig
	in	_____

p	it	pit
	ip	_____

s	in	sin
	ix	_____

s	ip	sip
	it	_____

r	ib	rib
	ip	_____

t	in	tin
	ip	_____

w	ig	wig
	in	_____

Word building with $\boxed{i}$

Read the words. Draw a picture.

Tim wins a bin. 	Jim in a big wig.
Six tins of pins.	A pig on a pin.
Pip's lips sip.	Kim hid Jim in the bin.

Word building with $\boxed{i}$

Wordsearch
Find 9 words with 'i' in them. Colour them yellow.

m	k	t	f	i	t	m	n	b	f	i	x
q	w	r	t	v	c	d	i	n	p	l	r
s	i	x	m	k	t	y	f	i	n	k	l
p	l	y	t	b	d	r	h	i	t	k	m
b	i	n	w	s	w	g	p	i	t	m	n
n	b	v	c	x	z	m	i	x	p	k	j

Did you find these words? Put them in the right boxes.

bin   hit   mix

fit   six   din

fin   pit   fix

__in	__it	__ix

Test 3

Write your name: _____

Write your name in the gaps. Read the sentences.

1. _____ hid a fig in a pit.

2. _____ can mix a lot of pins.

3. Can _____ fix the tin box?

4. _____ met a pig in a wig.

5. _____ had a six pins.

6. _____ can fit in the big bin.

Draw a picture for one sentence.

Circle the right word for the pictures below.

| bin | big | tin | tip | big | bib |
| wit | wig | pig | dig | sit | six |

Word building with o

Make new words. Write them on the lines.

h	og	hog
	op	_____
	ot	_____
	ob	_____

c	od	cod
	ot	_____
	op	_____
	og	_____

b	ox	box
	ob	_____
	og	_____

l	ot	lot
	ob	_____
	op	_____

Make new words. Write them on the lines.

d	**og**	dog
f		_____
c		_____
l		_____

h	**op**	hop
t		_____
m		_____
c		_____

r	**ob**	rob
j		_____
h		_____
s		_____

l	**ot**	lot
c		_____
g		_____
p		_____

Word building with o

Read the words. Draw a picture.

Tom hops on top of the box.	A pot of cogs.
A lot of hot dogs.	A cod and a mop in a cot.
The dog can jog on a log.	A hot fox in the fog.

Word building with o

Wordsearch
Find 9 words with 'o' in them. Colour them yellow.

p	l	k	i	c	o	p	m	h	k	u	y
d	o	g	m	n	b	c	b	h	f	o	g
z	x	w	s	d	j	o	b	m	n	k	j
x	h	o	p	m	k	j	t	o	p	k	m
k	c	o	g	b	n	m	h	o	b	w	q
q	w	t	y	d	x	r	o	b	j	g	q

Did you find these words? Put them in the right boxes.

cop	rob	job
fog	top	hop
hob	cog	dog

__og	__op	__ob

Test 4

Write your name: _____

Write your name in the gaps. Read the sentences.

1. _____ hops on top of a pot.

2. _____ has a lot of hot dogs.

3. _____ got a cod in a box.

4. _____ has got a job.

5. _____ has not got a mop.

6. _____ nods to Tom.

<table>
<tr><td>Draw a picture for one sentence.</td></tr>
</table>

Circle the right word for the pictures below.

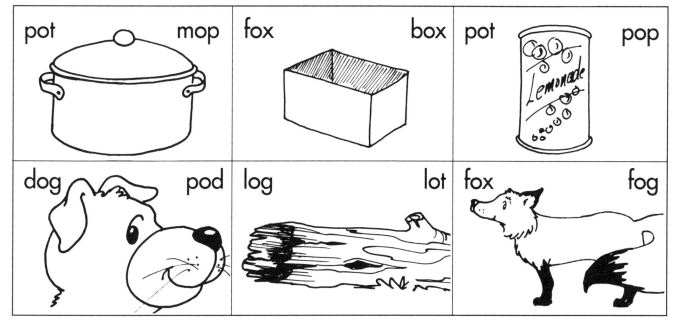

| pot   mop | fox   box | pot   pop |
| dog   pod | log   lot | fox   fog |

Word building with u

Make new words. Write them on the lines.

b	ud	bud		**h**	ub	hub
	ug	_____			ug	_____
	un	_____			um	_____
	ut	_____			ut	_____

s	um	sum		**p**	up	pup
	ub	_____			ug	_____
	un	_____			ut	_____
	ud	_____			un	_____

c		cub		m		mum
h		_____		r		_____
t	**ub**	_____		s	**um**	_____
r		_____		h		_____

c		cut		r		rug
j		_____		b		_____
n	**ut**	_____		m	**ug**	_____
h		_____		j		_____

Word building with  u

Read the words. Draw a picture.

Mum put the pup in the cup. 	A bun in the sun.
A pup has fun on a rug.	Mum dug in the mud.
Put the bug in the mug.	Cut the bun for Mum.

Word building with $\boxed{u}$

Wordsearch
Find 9 words with 'u' in them. Colour them yellow.

q	w	t	c	u	t	m	n	k	l	w	q
m	h	u	t	g	b	n	s	u	n	p	k
j	h	u	g	w	q	x	b	u	t	n	m
b	v	c	x	z	f	u	n	j	k	h	l
k	b	u	n	m	k	k	j	d	u	g	q
m	t	h	g	f	p	m	u	g	w	s	x

Did you find these words? Put them in the right boxes.

bun   fun   mug

hut   hug   cut

dug   but   sun

__ug	__ut	__un
___	___	___
___	___	___
___	___	___

UNDERSTANDING PHONICS – *Book 1*   © Folens (copiable page)

Test 5

Write your name: _____

Write your name in the gaps. Read the sentences.

1. _____ cut the hot bun.

2. _____ put a bug in Mum's cup.

3. Can _____ do ten sums on a bus?

4. _____ had fun on a rug with a pup.

5. _____ tugs the pup but the pup has
   fun in the mud.

6. Rub a dub dub put_____ in a tub.

Draw a picture for one sentence.

Circle the right word for the pictures below.

bun   bus   hug   jug   sun   sum

pup   put   mud   mug   bug   tug

Magic e with a

Make these into long 'a' sounds.

can   cane   pal   _____

mat   _____   rat   _____

mad   _____   pan   _____

hat   _____

Read the words. Draw a picture.

An ape in a cape.	A rat in a hat.
A man with a rake.	A cake on a mat.

Say all the words fast to make a silly rhyme.

Magic e with a

Read the sentences. Fill in the gaps with these words.

cat Sam	Sam had a h_____. He put it on the c_____.
hat sat	The c_____ got m_____. The c_____ s_____
mad	on the h_____.

Read the sentences. Fill the gaps with these words.

cake lane	1. Sam made a c _____ . He ate it up. It made him
case late	l_____ for school.
hate take	2. Dad said, "T_____ the c_____ and go up the l_____ ."
	"I h_____ c_____," said Dan. "T_____ it to Sam."

Read the sentences. Fill the gaps with these words.

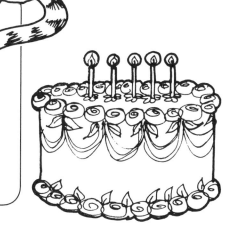

cat	1. Sam is my n_____ .
lane	2. My dad's n_____ is Pat.
name	3. We live in a l_____ .
rat	4. With a r_____ and a c_____ .

Read the rhyme.

Magic  e with a

Wordsearch
Find 12 words with a long 'a' sound. Colour them yellow.

i	l	b	u	f	a	d	e	x	g	m	k	m	d
r	y	n	a	m	e	l	i	p	a	n	e	f	w
o	p	g	h	a	t	e	k	u	h	t	o	p	h
b	e	l	a	t	e	q	s	a	m	e	k	c	t
m	o	p	t	a	k	e	b	l	a	n	e	s	k
p	u	d	a	t	e	f	c	a	s	e	w	p	u
b	n	y	c	a	k	e	t	m	a	k	e	c	t

Put the words in the right boxes.

rat   mad   fade
sat   lane   case
same   make   bat
name   cake   can
hate   hat   take
pal   gap   date
Sam   pan   fad
late   pane   mat

long 'a'	short 'a'

UNDERSTANDING PHONICS – *Book 1*   © Folens (copiable page)

Magic **e** with **a**

Write your name: _____

Write your name in the gaps. Read the sentences.

1. The rat made _____ mad.

2. "Take the cat to the gate, _____."

3. _____ made a cake for Sam.

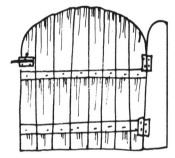

4. "Go to the lane, _____ . Take the rake."

5. The cake made _____ late for the date.

6. "Take a cake in case I'm late, _____ ."

Put the words in the right boxes.

made   take   gate   cake   lane   rake   late   date   case
fade   pane   sake   mane   cane   hate   mate   bake   rate

___ade	___ake	___ate	___ane	___ase

    UNDERSTANDING PHONICS – *Book 1*

Magic ☼e☼ with o

Make these into long 'o' sounds.

cod   code   rod   _____

rob   _____   cop   _____

hop   _____   pop   _____

Read the words. Draw a picture.

A hog in a robe.	A mole in a hole.
A rose on the nose.	A dog up a pole.

Say all the words fast to make a silly rhyme.

     © Folens (copiable page)

Magic e with o

Read the sentences. Fill in the gaps with these words.

dog pot lot hot	Tom had a d_____ . He fed it on h_____ p_____. It had a l_____ .

Read the sentences. Fill the gaps with these words.

hole wore mole rose pole joke	1. Tom had a big h_____ in his cap. He got wet. 2. Kim w_____'a r_____ . 3. The m_____ is up the p_____ for a j_____ .

Read the sentences. Fill the gaps with these words.

hole rose mole pole	1. The _____ can hop into a _____ . 2. The man wore a _____ . 3. A cat can run up a _____ .

Read the rhyme.

Magic *e* with ☐ **o**

Wordsearch
Find 12 words with a long 'o' sound. Colour them yellow.

p	x	n	o	t	e	k	l	h	o	s	e	z	k
s	o	r	e	m	h	f	b	h	o	m	e	j	t
t	h	w	q	j	o	k	e	w	t	c	o	n	e
x	c	o	p	e	k	m	t	s	o	l	e	z	g
p	o	k	e	v	h	t	r	w	r	o	s	e	v
j	k	l	b	o	n	e	l	k	y	m	o	l	e

Put the words in the right boxes.

cod   jot   sore

home   fox   dog

box   hose   sole

joke   poke   got

note   log   mop

cone   cope   not

hop   top   dot

mole   rose   bone

long 'o'	short 'o'

UNDERSTANDING PHONICS – *Book 1*

© Folens (copiable page)

Magic ✳e✳ with ⬚o⬚

Write your name: _____

Write your name in the gaps. Read the sentences.

1. _____ woke up.

2. _____ had a mole at home.

3. "Let the dog have the bone, _____ ."

4. _____ had a cone and a hot dog.

5. "Get a rose, _____ ."

6. _____ had a red nose for a joke.

Put the words in the right boxes.

joke	rose	hole	wore	cone
core	bone	hose	coke	sole
poke	pole	tone	sore	nose

___ose	___oke	___ole	___one	___ore

Magic e with u and i

Make these into long 'u' sounds (add an e).

cub   cube   tub   _____

cut   _____   us   _____

Read the words. Draw a picture.

A cat in a cube.	A line of a tune.
Mum on a mule.	A ripe plum in June.

Say all the words fast to make a silly rhyme.

Magic 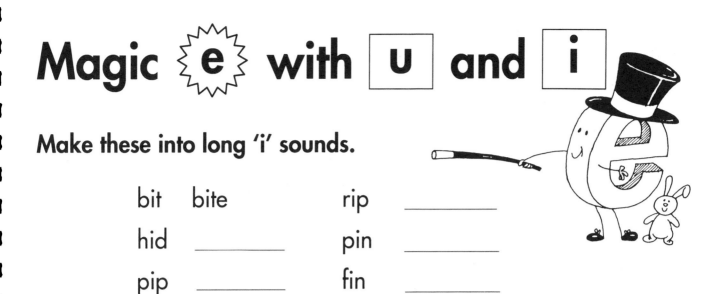 e with u and i

Make these into long 'i' sounds.

bit   bite   rip   _____

hid   _____   pin   _____

pip   _____   fin   _____

Read the words. Draw a picture.

Five red kites.	A pup rides a bike.
A mule bites Mum.	June on a hike.

Say all the words fast to make a silly rhyme.

     UNDERSTANDING PHONICS – Book 1

Magic  e with u and i

Wordsearch
Find 6 words with long 'u' sounds and colour them yellow. Find 6 words with long 'i' sounds and colour them red.

p	x	m	c	u	b	e	m	b	c	r	u	l	e
t	u	n	e	q	w	a	s	r	i	d	e	w	t
x	z	s	l	c	u	t	e	x	y	t	u	b	e
h	i	d	e	p	r	i	p	e	b	i	t	e	d
k	j	p	u	r	e	t	b	i	k	e	e	j	k
l	x	f	e	v	b	c	t	i	m	e	d	s	w

Put the words in the right boxes.

cube   mile   rule
life   tube   wire
cure   bite   mute
ripe   time   sure
tide   tune   five
cute   like   mule
hide   fuse   pipe
rude   bike   pure

long 'u'	long 'i'

Magic e with u and i

Write your name: _____

Write your name in the gaps. Read the sentences.

1. _____ had a cute cat.

2. _____ sat in the sun in June.

3. "Let _____ use the red cube."

4. _____ has a fine bike.

5. _____ can dive off the side.

6. _____ rides for five miles.

Put the words in the right boxes.

mile   tube   tile   side   wide   site   tide   cure   kite
sure   file   bite   pure   ride   bike   like   cube   hide

__ile	__ite	__ide	__ike	__ure	__ube

UNDERSTANDING PHONICS – *Book 1*

Blending two consonants

Write new words on the lines. Think of another word for each list.

sh
op _____
ed _____
ut _____

sh _____

ch
ip _____
ess _____
op _____

ch _____

th
is _____
en _____
ink _____

th _____

wh
at _____
en _____
ich _____
ere _____
ip _____

wh _____

qu
een _____
iz _____
it _____
ite _____
ilt _____

qu _____

ck
ba _____
ki _____
so _____
ne _____
sa _____

_____ ck

th
too _____
ba _____
wi _____

_____ th

sh
ma _____
fi _____
pu _____

_____ sh

ch
cat _____
ben _____
hit _____

_____ ch

UNDERSTANDING PHONICS – *Book 1*   © Folens (copiable page)

Blending two consonants

Wordsearch
Find 12 words beginning with 'sh', 'qu', 'ch' and 'th'.
Colour each word.

w	t	r	s	h	o	p	b	n	q	u	e	e	n
s	h	e	l	l	x	c	v	c	h	u	m	l	k
q	u	a	c	k	x	r	t	t	h	i	n	b	n
m	n	b	q	u	i	e	t	k	j	s	h	u	t
t	h	i	r	t	y	k	m	j	c	h	e	s	s
m	x	t	h	e	n	z	k	w	c	h	o	p	j

Put the words in the right boxes.

child	quiz	chess	queen
quick	then	shed	shall
chick	shell	thin	chop
quack	that	quilt	shut
ship	thank	shop	chum
chip	quiet	thirty	there

ch_____	sh_____	qu_____	th_____

UNDERSTANDING PHONICS – *Book 1*

Blending two consonants

Here is a tongue twister. Try to say it fast.
Cut out the tongue twister. Stick it on to the fish's face.

A posh fish chops chips in a fish shop.

(You can curl the tongue with a pencil.)

Say these tongue twisters and draw pictures of them.

Which whale whistles, which whale whispers?	Six shells shine on a sunny shore.
Wash a sack of posh socks in a sock shop.	Six chums in a church chess match.

Make up your own tongue twister.

Blending two consonants

Find the words that begin with 'sh', 'ch', 'wh', 'th' and 'qu'.
There are 4 of each. Put the words in the right boxes.

shell	what	chum	where
quiz	three	chop	queen
when	shop	think	chip
chess	that	quack	than
she	quiet	ship	which

sh_____	ch_____	wh_____	th_____	qu_____

Put in the missing words.

1.	chess	chum	Sam played _____ with his _____.
2.	shells	beach	Kim got five _____ on the _____.
3.	think	thin	I _____ the cat is too _____.
4.	cloth	shed	Put the _____ in the _____.
5.	queen	quilt	The _____ likes the red _____.

Vowels followed by r

Write 'ar' in the spaces. Say the words.

c_____ c_____d p_____k b_____ h_____d m_____k

Write 'er' in the spaces. Say the words.

bett_____ sist_____ long_____ bigg_____ broth_____ short_____

Write 'ir' in the spaces. Say the words.

s_____ d_____t b_____d g_____l sh_____t th_____d

Write 'or' in the spaces. Say the words.

f_____ b_____n s_____t f_____k c_____n sh_____t

Write 'ur' in the spaces. Say the words.

f_____ b_____n p_____se h_____t t_____n n_____se

Circle the right word for the pictures below.

| card | cart | better | letter | fork | horse |
| churn | nurse | shirt | bird | shark | short |

40   UNDERSTANDING PHONICS – Book 1   © Folens (copiable page)

Vowels followed by r

Wordsearch
Find 12 words with 'ar', 'er', 'ir' or 'or'.
Colour each word.

b	a	r	x	z	d	f	o	r	k	l	l	k	e
m	h	e	r	d	z	j	s	i	r	x	w	q	u
k	m	j	a	r	p	j	l	o	r	d	t	y	z
p	a	f	t	e	r	g	d	i	r	t	g	r	a
s	h	i	r	t	x	c	a	r	y	k	e	x	s
z	b	e	t	t	e	r	f	o	r	m	j	t	i

Put the words in the right boxes.

bar fern jar short
fork park girl better
dirt mark after form
part morning letter car
cork sir her shirt
bird herd lord firm

ar	or	ir	er

UNDERSTANDING PHONICS – Book 1

Vowels followed by r

Underline the right words.

1. Kim wore a red (shirt short).

2. Let's go in the (car cur).

3. Put the (nurse purse) in a pocket.

4. The (first thirst) bus is here.

5. The teacher likes summer (butter better) than winter.

Make three more sentences. Use these words.

bird _____

car _____

nurse _____

Read the words. Draw a picture.

A girl with a fork.	A bird on a church.
A shark in the park.	A dirty shirt.

Vowels followed by r

Put in the missing words.

1.	birds	forest	Forty _____ in a dark _____ .
2.	farm	better	Can the _____ dog bark _____ ?
3.	card	forget	Don't _____ the birthday _____ .
4.	thirsty	third	The _____ bird is _____ .
5.	Saturday	hurt	Tom _____ his arm on _____ .
6.	purse	nurse	The _____ had a fur _____ .

Make two more sentences using these words.

farm _____

fork _____

Draw pictures to match your sentences.

More consonant blends

Write new words on the lines. Think of another word for each list.

br
- at   brat
- ed   _____
- im   _____
- oth   _____
- ush   _____

br _____

cr
- ab   crab
- ess   _____
- ib   _____
- op   _____
- ust   _____

cr _____

sl
- ap   slap
- ender   _____
- ip   _____
- og   _____
- ug   _____

sl _____

pr
- am   pram
- ess   _____
- im   _____
- op   _____
- une   _____

pr _____

tr
- ap   trap
- end   _____
- ip   _____
- ot   _____
- uck   _____

tr _____

cl
- ap   clap
- ever   _____
- iff   _____
- ock   _____
- ub   _____

cl _____

fl
- ap   flap
- ed   _____
- ip   _____
- og   _____
- uff   _____

fl _____

gl
- ad   glad
- en   _____
- itter   _____
- oss   _____
- um   _____

gl _____

dr
- ag   drag
- ess   _____
- ill   _____
- op   _____
- um   _____

dr _____

More consonant blends

Complete the rhyming words. Read them aloud.

clap	trend	drip	crab	brush	crop
sl_____	bl _____	tr_____	dr_____	fl_____	dr _____
tr _____			gr_____		fl _____
					sl _____

Find the words that begin with the same 2 letters.
There are 3 of each.
Write them on the lines below.

slush	clip	fled	glum	grid	blush
clever	blade	slide	grime	cloth	track
blister	problem	glide	drip	plod	fluff
tree	pram	flick	green	slap	dress
plum	glad	truck	pride	plan	drag

sl _____	slush _____	slide _____	slap _____
cl _____	clever _____	_____	_____
_____	_____	_____	_____
_____	_____	_____	_____
_____	_____	_____	_____
_____	_____	_____	_____
_____	_____	_____	_____
_____	_____	_____	_____

More consonant blends

Here is a tongue twister. Try to say it fast.
Cut out the tongue twister. Stick it on to the crab's face.

A
cross crab
crashed across
a cress crop.

(You can curl the tongue with a pencil.)

Here are some tongue twisters to say fast. Draw pictures for them.

A slick slug slid on a slippery slope.	The class clapped as clever Clint cleared the cliff.
Grumpy Greg grunts and grabs the green gremlin.	The freckled frog fries fresh fritters.

Make up your own tongue twister.

More consonant blends

Circle the first two letters of these words in different colours.

cr = blue   br = red

pl = yellow   tr = black

dr = green

cricket	brim	drive	dram	crime	drill	bride
brunch	crept	broth	trend	crop	crust	trench
trolley	crock	dresser	plush	bronze	please	play
breeze	dregs	trumpet	trash	drum	crest	cress
drag	plant	cross	plenty	drape	tree	plop

Put in the missing words.

1. presents crib	tree plenty	At Christmas we have a _____, a Christmas _____ and _____ of _____.
2. blob glue	broke cricket	Brenda _____ the _____ bat. It needed a _____ of _____.
3. frost sleet	gloves	I wear _____ when it is cold and there is _____ and _____.

Make two more sentences. Use these words.

clock   broke   plum   slug

_____

_____

Revision test

Write your name in the gaps. Read the sentences.

1. _____ has a hat.
2. Let _____ get a red pen.
3. _____ hops on top of a pot.
4. _____ tugs the pup but the pup has fun in the mud.
5. _____ can fit in the big bin.

Put the words in the right boxes.

rake   date   bite   tube   poke   bake
hate   cube   nose   kite   rose   joke

___ake	___ate	___ite	___ube	___oke	___ose

Read all the words. Fill the gaps with the right words.

1.	think	thin	I_____ the cat is too_____ .
2.	queen	quilt	The _____ likes the red_____ .
3.	card	forget	Don't _____ the birthday_____ .
4.	thirsty	third	The _____ bird is _____ .
5.	Saturday	hurt	Tom _____ his arm on _____ .
6.	presents tree plenty		At Christmas we have a Christmas _____ and _____ of _____ .

     UNDERSTANDING PHONICS – *Book 1*   © Folens (copiable page)